Playtime and Storytime

COMPILED BY
CAROL M. LANE

HART PUBLISHING COMPANY, INC. • NEW YORK

Playtime *and* Storytime

Contents

Wide and Narrow

HOUSE 1 IS WIDE. HOUSE 2 IS NARROW.

COLOR WIDE WINDOW RED. COLOR NARROW WINDOW GREEN.

COLOR WIDE CAGES YELLOW. COLOR NARROW CAGES RED.

WRITE 1 IN THE WIDE BOTTLE. WRITE 2 IN NARROW BOTTLES.

The Toy Shop

Betty's birthday is coming soon. Just in case her Mommy should ask her what she'd like to have for a present, Betty is looking at all the toys in the toy shop. What would *you* like to have?

What winter toys are there in the store? What summer toys? Which are riding toys? Do you see any writing toys? Would you like to own a toy shop?

Follow the Dots

Take your pencil and start on dot number one. Draw a line from dot one to dot two. Continue from one dot to another until you have made a complete picture.

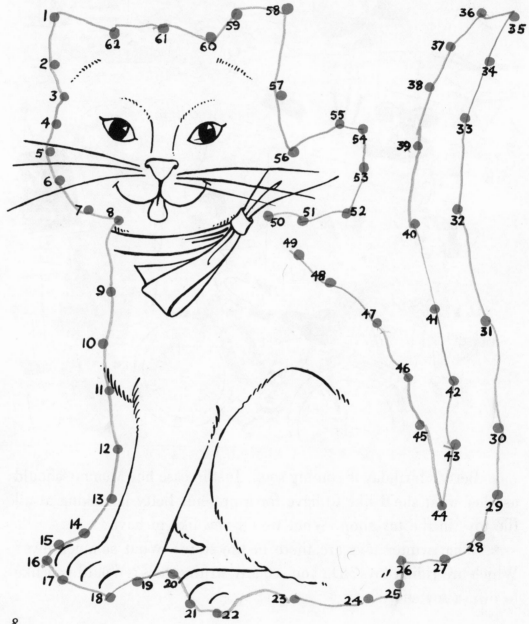

Mysterious the Mouse

BY CAROLINE HOROWITZ

JOANIE loved pets. She had a pet puppy, a pet pussy, a pet canary, and a pet mousie.

She kept her pet puppy in a cute little dog house in the yard. She named her puppy, Peppy.

She kept her pet canary in a pretty cage in the living-room. She called her canary, Carrie.

She kept her pet pussy in a cozy basket in the kitchen. She called her pussy, Purry.

But when it came to her pet mouse, she didn't keep him *anywhere at all!* All for a very good reason! She simply couldn't catch him! Oh, she saw him very often—practically every day. Sometimes she would come into her bedroom and there he'd be, sitting on the window sill, munching on a bit of cracker.

He wouldn't run away, when he saw her—he'd just cock his head to one side, as if to say, "Hello, look who's here!"

As a matter of fact, that's just what Joanie would say often when she saw *him*: "Hello, look who's here!"

Other times, she would meet him in the bathroom or in the attic, where she went to play on rainy days. She would talk to him, and he would squeak back to her. He was so friendly and unafraid, but he would *never* stay still — so that she might pick him up and stroke him, as she did with her other pets. The minute she reached out to touch him, away he scurried!

She told everyone in the family about him, because he was so mysterious. In fact, that's what she named her mousie. She called him Mysterious the Mouse.

One day, she said to her big brother, Michael, "Oh, Michael, I *do* wish Mysterious, my mousie, would stop being so mysterious. I can see my other pets whenever I want to. I feed them and say good-night to them every night. Peppy, my puppy, Carrie, my canary, and Purry, my pussy, are *always* here; but Mysterious, my mousie, is here one minute and gone the next. If he would only stay with me,

I'd build him the nicest little mouse house, right here in my own room."

"I wish I could help you, Joanie," said Michael. "I'll think and think and maybe I'll be able to figure out a way to make Mysterious want to stay with us always."

When Joanie went to sleep that night, it seemed to her she had just closed her eyes, when she heard music. She opened her eyes and listened. Someone was playing on her little toy piano, right in her room!

She sat up in bed and looked. Guess who it was? It was Mysterious the Mouse, running up and down along the piano keys. Joan laughed in glee.

"Hello, look who's here!" she said.

Mysterious stopped for a moment, cocked his head to one side, as if to say, "Hello, yourself!" But then he began running up and down again along the keys of her toy piano. He made the prettiest music.

"Michael, Michael," called Joanie, "Please come here. Quick!"

Michael came running to the door of her room. He stopped

when he saw what was happening for he didn't want to frighten Mysterious away.

"Joanie," he whispered, "I think my plan worked. I put little pieces of cheese on the keys of your toy piano, hoping that Mysterious would come to eat them, and he *did* come. He's eaten up all the cheese, but he seems to have fallen in love with the sound of the music that he makes. Maybe, *maybe*, he'll stay!"

After a few minutes, Mysterious got a little tired of running along the piano keys. But did he run away? No siree! He just snuggled down inside the little toy piano and made his home there. Joanie made it nice and cozy inside the piano, with a layer of soft paper napkins. She fed him cheese and crackers.

Every morning, she woke up to the sound of the music that Mysterious the Mouse made by running up and down the keys of the little piano. And every night he played a little good night tune, before he snuggled down to sleep in his little piano bed.

Clothespin Fence

Materials: Clothespins

You can do so many things with clothespins. Here is a clothespin play idea that is easy and lots of fun.

Slide one clothespin into the other, as shown in the small picture. The clothespins will look like the letter *X*. Make a few of these, and then set them up in a row. Lay a line of clothespins across them. The crossed clothespins will stand up firmly, forming a fence.

Matching Shapes

In each row of pictures, two shapes are exactly alike. Can you pick them out?

Wishes

I want to be a bird, I do
    And fly, and fly, and fly
Way, way up above the trees
    High, high, high.

I want to be a fish, I do
    Deep down I would go
In a little pool I'd swim and dive
    Low, low, low.

I want to be so many things
    But I don't ever see
Just how I can be anything
    Except just ME.

Primrose L. Hooper

Cowboy

Take your pencil and start on dot number one. Draw a line from dot one to dot two. Continue from one dot to another until you have made a complete picture.

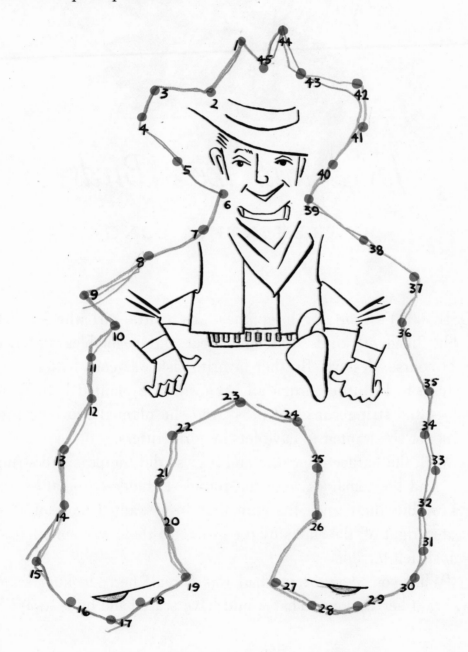

Josie and the Birds

BY CLEMENTINA LONG

JOSIE (that's short for Josephine) was a little girl who loved to eat. She liked *all* kinds of food — meat and vegetables and fruit and, of course, dessert! But her favorite dish was corn fritters.

Josie had a little garden all her own. She planted lettuce and tomatoes and stringbeans and peas. And she planted two long rows of corn, for she wanted to have lots of corn fritters.

Well, the lettuce grew nice and big; so did the peas and stringbeans. And the tomatoes were the roundest, reddest, tomatoes you ever saw. But the corn — the corn that Josie wanted most of all — was eaten right off the stalks by the birds, till there was none left.

Josie felt terrible.

"What you *should* have had was a real, fierce-looking scarecrow," said her Daddy. "That would have scared the birds away!"

Josie's Mommy went to town and bought corn at the vegetable store. She made Josie a whole batch of corn fritters. Josie thanked her Mommy, and she certainly loved the corn fritters. (Who wouldn't, with piles of delicious maple syrup poured all over them!) But she couldn't help feeling disappointed that her *own* corn was eaten up by the birds.

Well, Fall came; then Winter; and pretty soon it was Springtime again.

"This time," said Josie,"I'm going to make the fiercest-looking scarecrow in the world. And I just dare those birds to *touch* my corn."

So she planted ten whole rows of corn. Then her Daddy helped her make a scarecrow. It sure was a fierce scarecrow!

The birds were so scared they didn't go *near* the corn. They would fly around and perch on the nearby trees and bushes and chirp angrily.

But Josie said, "This is *my* corn. I planted and I'm taking care of it. I love corn fritters and this time I'm going to have stacks and stacks of them. So just you go away and stop making all that racket."

When the corn was ripe, Josie picked it all. There was so much corn that it filled four big baskets.

The first night, Josie's Mommy made a great big platter full of corn fritters. Josie ate so much she thought she would burst. Her Mommy and Daddy and Aunt Elizabeth all had big portions, too. And there still were three and a half baskets of corn left.

They had corn fritters every day for four days, till they simply couldn't look at another corn fritter. Josie gave corn to Aunt Elizabeth to take home with her. She also gave some to the poor old lady who lived down the lane. But she still had a basket and a half left.

"You ought to scrape the corn off the stalks and put it away to dry," said Josie's Daddy. "Then some day during the winter we can make pop-corn. We can have a Pop-corn Party."

"Oh, yes! Let's do that!" said Josie. So they dried the corn and put it away.

Soon the summer was over and it grew cold. Most of the birds flew away, down to the warm Southlands.

One cold day, Josie's Daddy said to her, "How about a Pop-corn Party? Let's build a campfire out near the barn and pop the corn there."

Josie helped her Daddy find a big pile of wood for the fire. Pretty soon they were all sitting near the barn, singing songs and eating pop-corn. The fire burned brightly and kept them warm.

And then Josie suddenly noticed some little birds hopping around in the snow. Whenever a few kernels of corn fell on the ground, they would swoop down and gobble them up.

"Poor things!" said Josie. "They must be hungry. With the snow covering everything, how do they get anything to eat?"

"Lots of them can't find anything to eat and they starve and die," said her Daddy.

"What!" cried Josie. "And me with all this corn! Let's stop popping corn this minute. I'm going to give all my corn to the birds right now!"

So that's how the birds finally got Josie's corn. Not in the Summertime when they had all they needed to eat. Not when they took it without permission. But when Josie saw that they were cold and hungry in the Winter, then she was *glad* to give them her corn.

Playmate

Lively   *Action song*

Oh come on play - mate, ____ Come on and

Beckon with
your finger.

Fold your arms and rock
them back and forth.

Then hold up
three fingers.

play with me, ____ And bring your dol - lies three. ____ Climb up my

Pretend you are climbing a tree.

Cup your hands around your mouth.

ap - ple   tree.___ Shout down my | rain   barrel ___ Slide down my

Place your hands next to each other and slide them downwards together.

Wave your hand as if in greeting.

cel - lar door,___ And we'll be | jol - ly   friends___ For - ev - er   more.

Longer and Shorter

WHICH IS LONGER, THE KITE STRING OR THE BALLOON STRING?

WHOSE WAGON IS SHORTER, BETTY'S OR JACK'S?

WHOSE TRAIN IS SHORTER, MARY'S OR TED'S?

WHOSE SHOVEL IS LONGER, DICK'S OR JOAN'S?

Pies

My Mommy rolls the dough out flat
    And sprinkles out the flour,
And then she puts the apples in
    And bakes her pie an hour.

And when she takes it out again,
    It's such a lovely pie!
It smells so good, and tastes so good
    That Daddy says, "My, my!"

    The pies we make are pretty too,
        Sally and me and Bud;
    I wish that we could eat them up
        But they're just made of mud!

Albert B. Southwick

Humpty Dumpty

Materials: A hardboiled egg
                  Crayons
                  A small box

Boil a nice white egg until it is thoroughly hard. Now draw the simple features and clothes which you see pictured here, on the white egg shell. The shell of an egg takes crayons, paints, pencil, or ink equally well.

Now take a small box and color it to look like a brick wall. Make a small hole in the top of the box so that *Humpty Dumpty* can sit on the wall. This hole should not be too big for you'll want *Humpty* to fall off easily.

When you come to the part of the poem that goes, *"Humpty Dumpty had a great fall!"* give *Humpty* a little push. He'll tumble off the wall!

Things We Work With

Can you tell what each thing is used for?

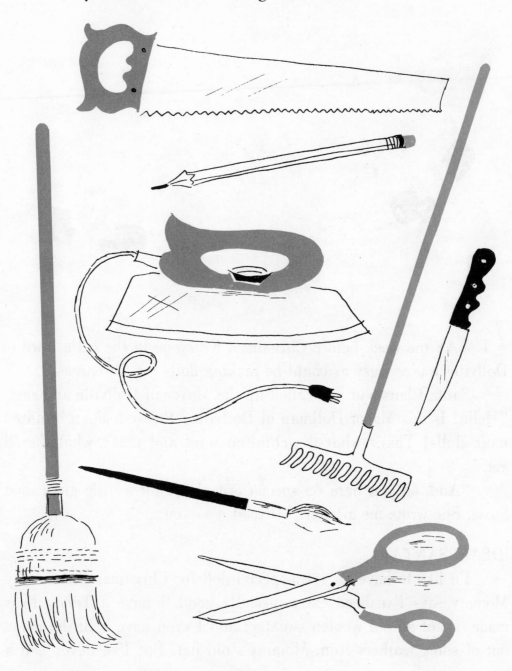

The Extra-Special Doll

BY CAROLINE HOROWITZ

*I*T WAS the week before Christmas. Everyone in the little town of Dollville was as busy as could be making dolls for Christmas.

Santa Claus had just called up the Mayor of Dollville and said, "Hello! Is this Mayor Dollman of Dollville? Please make a hundred more dolls! That's what the children want and that's what they'll get."

"And, oh yes, here's a *special* order! It's for a little girl called Susie. She wrote me a letter. I'll read it to you:

'DEAR SANTA:

I'd like to have an extra-special doll for Christmas because my Mommy says I've been extra-specially good. I have a Teddy Bear made out of an old woolen sweater; and I even have a Birdie made out of some feathers from Mommy's old hat. But I've never had a store doll, and even though I love my toys very much, I'd like to have a doll that comes from a store. I shall name her Geraldine.

Thanking you in advance, I am

Your loving admirer,

Susie Michaels'

"Did you hear *that?*" said Santa Claus. Now I want you people in Dollville to make Susie the most *extra-special* doll in the world. I'll leave it to you. You know all about dolls. Good-bye now, I must call up Sledville to see about ordering some sleds. Good-bye."

The people of Dollville thought and thought. They knew how to make dolls that walked and dolls that talked. They knew how to make sleeping dolls and even drinking dolls. Those were all *special* dolls. But Santa Claus had said that he wanted an *extra*-special doll.

"Leave it to me," said the Mayor's wife. "I'll figure out something."

Mrs. Dollman would not tell anyone how she was going to make Susie's doll extra-special. And everyone in Dollville was so busy that they didn't have time to ask her.

Well, Christmas came and soon Christmas was over.

It was just about a week after Christmas that the telephone rang. It was Santa Claus. He asked to speak to Mrs. Dollman. When she came to the phone he said, "Mrs. Dollman, you know lots of children write to me before Christmas to tell me what they want for Christmas. And I'm very happy when I can get them what they want. But here's a little girl who writes to me *after* Christmas to thank me for what she got. I thought you'd like to hear this letter:

'My darling, darling Santa:

Thank you a million times for my wonderful extra-special doll! I got up early Christmas morning and rushed downstairs. Sure enough, there was the most beautiful doll in the world, right under the Christmas tree. She had golden curls and big blue eyes. When I sat her up, she said *Ma-Ma;* when I laid her down she closed her eyes to sleep; when I gave her some water out of her bottle, she drank it right down.

I was so happy with her that I picked her up and hugged her, and said, *"I love you so, my beautiful Geraldine."* Then the most

30

marvelous thing happened: My dolly said, *"I love you too!"*

Santa dear, I don't know how it happens; whether there is a button somewhere in my doll's back that gets squeezed when I hug her. If there is, *I* can't find it. But I *do* know that every time I hug her she says, *"I love you, too!"* It is so wonderful to hear my dolly say she loves me, just when I am loving her!

Thank you, dear Santa Claus, for my wonderful extra-special doll.

Your loving friend,
Susie' "

What's Wrong with this Shop?

It's no wonder Mr. Beefer looks so puzzled. He's supposed to be running a butcher shop, but he sees quite a number of things that don't belong in his shop. Can you pick them out?

Pick the Picture

The questions on this page are fun to answer. The pictures show the answers. Can you pick out the right picture for each question?

WHAT LIVES ON A FARM? WHAT IS USED FOR CARRYING THINGS?

WHAT IS USED WHEN IT RAINS? WHAT IS USED FOR WRITING?

WHAT IS USED IN A BEDROOM? WHAT IS USED FOR CLIMBING?

WHAT JUMPS THROUGH THE TREES? WHAT SWIMS IN THE WATER?

Enchanted Castle

Here's a very interesting maze. Do you know what a maze is? A maze is a secret winding path that leads to a hidden place.

In the picture, you will see an enchanted castle. There are many paths in the picture. It is up to you to find your way into the Enchanted Castle. Can you do it? You solve this maze by putting your pencil on the opening marked START. You must not cross any solid lines. You may only move in the white spaces.

Patty's Secret

BY MARTHA L. NOME

$\mathcal{P}$ATTY loved to play on the beach. Every day, in the summertime, her mother used to take her there — that is, every sunny day. When it rained, Patty stayed at home.

Patty loved to dig in the sand. Don't you? She made all kinds of shapes with her sand set — sand pies and sand towers and all sorts of things.

One day, she made a beautiful sand castle with gardens and roads and towers and even a tunnel leading to the castle. It was so big and beautiful she hoped it would never get broken down. Most of the time Patty didn't care very much if the things she made got spoiled. In fact, many times she broke them down herself. But she wanted this castle to stay just the way it was, forever.

She asked her mother to make a sign saying, PLEASE DON'T TOUCH. She stuck the sign in the sand right in front of her castle. Then it was time to go home.

Next day, she hurried back to the beach to see her sand castle. But when she got there, she saw that her beautiful sand castle was all spoiled. None of the children had touched it; but the waves had come up during the night and washed away almost the whole castle. All that was left of it was just a little hill of sand.

Patty felt so badly, she felt like crying. She didn't even feel like building another one.

She went into the water and swam around for a little while. But pretty soon she got tired of swimming, and she felt like digging in the sand again. But she didn't feel like just making little pies any more. You know how it is, once you make something big and important, like a sand castle; it's not much fun just making little things any more.

Then she got an idea. She'd make *another* castle; but *this* time she'd make it out of sea-shells. Then the waves couldn't wash it away.

So she gathered a whole basketful of shells. Then she picked a spot, way in from the water. She began to build her sea-shell castle.

It wasn't so easy. By the end of the afternoon, when she had to go home, she hadn't quite finished. But she didn't care. She wanted to build it up slowly, and make it really beautiful.

When she came back the next day, there it was — just the way she'd left it the night before. The waves had not spoiled it, and Patty was so happy.

It took all day until it was finished. But it was the most beautiful little castle you ever saw. Everybody came to look at it. They couldn't get over it.

"It's so lovely, we ought to take a picture of it!" said her Daddy.

"Why, if I were a tiny fairy princess, that's just the castle I would want to live in!" said her mother.

Patty was so in love with her sea-shell castle that she came to the beach every single morning just to play with it.

One morning, she came to the beach especially early. Nobody else was there yet. She ran to her castle and knelt down in front of it.

And then she saw something wonderful! A beautiful little mermaid was in her castle!

A mermaid is a pretty lady down to her waist; but instead of having legs, she has a fish's tail. A mermaid lives in the ocean. She can swim just like a fish because of her fish's tail.

This tiny mermaid had long, golden hair and sea-blue eyes and she had the prettiest face. She was only three inches long — just the right size for Patty's sea-shell castle.

"Oh, you pretty darling!" cried Patty. "I hope you like your castle."

"I do, very much," said the tiny little mermaid, in a tiny little voice. "I'd like to live here always. But nobody must know except you. Otherwise, I will not live here. I'm not afraid of you because you built me this lovely castle."

"You're right; you don't have to be afraid of me, you darling little mermaid," said Patty. "What's your name?"

My name is Sea-Flower," said the tiny mermaid in her tiny, little voice. "And what's yours?"

"My name is Patty. And I promise I won't tell anybody that you're living in my sea-shell castle. But can't I even tell Mommy?"

"Well, I'll think it over and let you know tomorrow," said the mermaid.

Patty didn't tell anybody about the beautiful little mermaid; and during the day, the mermaid hid inside the castle whenever anyone else came near.

When the end of the afternoon came and it was time to go home, Patty bent down to the little mermaid, and whispered, "Good-night, Sea-Flower."

Sea-Flower peeked out of one of the castle windows and answered, "Good-night, Patty."

Next day, when Patty came to her sea-shell castle, Sea-Flower was waiting for her. "You may tell your Mommy about me, but nobody else," said Sea-Flower.

When Patty's Mommy met Sea-Flower, she loved her just as much as Patty did. And Patty's Mommy didn't tell a soul about Sea-Flower either.

Sea-Flower lived in the beautiful sea-shell castle all summer and nobody on the whole beach knew about it except Patty and her Mommy.

At the end of the summer, when it began to get chilly, little Sea-Flower said, "It's time for me to swim down South where the water is warm. I must say good-bye, now. But next summer, when you come back to the beach, I'll come back too. I'll be waiting for you in this beautiful sea-shell castle you built for me."

"Good-bye, Sea-Flower," said Patty. "I'll be waiting for you next summer."

Add to the Pictures

How many flowers are in this jar ? Add enough to make 5.

How many lollypops are in this jar ? Add enough to make 6.

How many marbles are in this dish? Add enough to make 9.

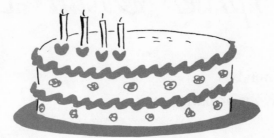

How many candles are on this cake? Add enough to make 8.

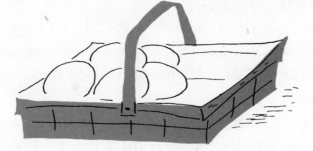

How many eggs are in this basket? Add enough to make 7.

How many cherries are on this plate? Add enough to make 4.

How many pencils are on this table? Add enough to make 10.

Surprise Mail Box

Materials: A shoe-box

Crayons or paints

Having to stay in bed is not so hard if Mother will give you this *Surprise Mail Box.*

Take a shoe box and decorate it prettily with crayons or paints. Place it next to the bed. Then while you are sleeping at night or having a nap during the day, Mother will place some nice gift in the *Surprise Mail Box.*

You'll never know what surprises you'll find in it when you wake up—a game, a toy, a get-well card, a new book, or some goodies —it might be anything. Nobody minds going to sleep or even taking sour medicine, if he knows that there'll always be a surprise waiting for him in the *Surprise Mail Box.*

Four Kittens

Marjorie and Marian, Mary and Mabel
Are four little kittens that live in our stable.

Marjorie's white as a saucer of milk.
Marian's hair is soft as grey silk.

Mary looks much like a tiger, but Mabel
Is the blackest cat in our old stable.

And I am happy as happy can be
Since Daddy gave all those kittens to me.

I feed them warm milk right fresh from the dairy —
Marjorie, Marian, Mabel and Mary!

Enola Chamberlin

Looby-Loo

Gay   *Circle action song*

Here we go Loo-by Loo, Here we go Loo-by Light,

Here we go Loo-by Loo, All on a Sat-ur-day

44

Point your right foot in front of you.

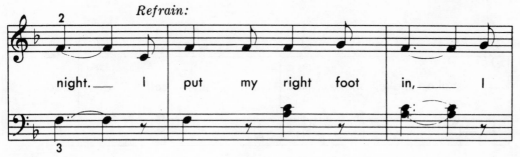

Refrain:

night.___ I put my right foot in,___ I

Point your right foot behind you.

Shake your right foot.

put my right foot out,___ I give my right foot a

Now turn around
just once

shake, shake, shake, And | turn my self a - | bout.

2. I put my left foot in
3. I put my right hand in
4. I put my left hand in
5. I put my little head in
6. I put my whole self in

(Circle round for Looby-Loo.
Then stand face inside of circle and follow actions.)

Traffic

In summertime our garden walk
Is like a busy street;
So many bugs run up and down
With tiny little feet.

The ants are shiny taxicabs,
Oh, my! They go so fast!
Here comes a caterpillar bus
Who slowly travels past.

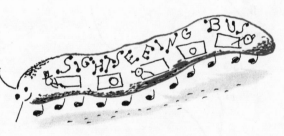

I'm very sure that bugs must have
Some very special vision;
For I have never, never seen
A bugmobile collision!

Jane Lear Talley

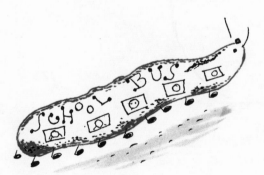

Squirrel

Take your pencil and start on dot number one. Draw a line from dot one to dot two. Continue from one dot to another until you have made a complete picture.

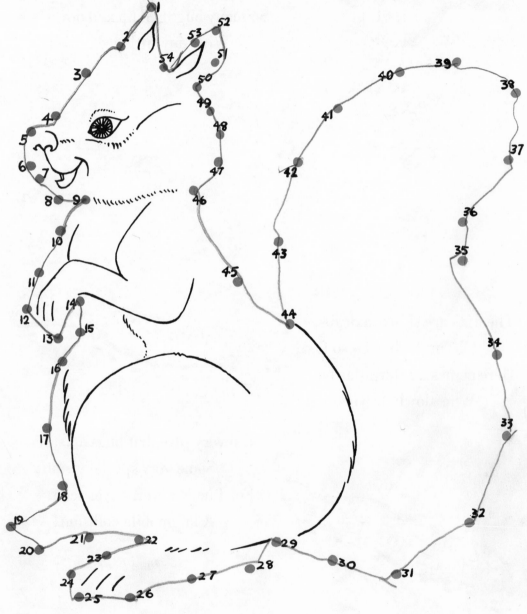

Pete the Peanut Man

Materials: 6 peanuts
                 A needle and thread
                 Some crayons or ink

Make a nice big knot on the end of a double thread. Just sew some peanuts together, using one peanut as the body, two for the legs, two for the arms, and a small one for the head.

Draw a jolly, little face on the head—and there you are!

You can tie a piece of cord to the knot on the head and make *Pete the Peanut Man* dance on his string. You can sew him on to a ribbon-bow, attach a safety-pin to the back of the bow, and wear him on your coat lapel. He'll really be cute.

Where's My Mister Fuzzy?

I can't find Mr. Fuzzy,
    And I've looked high and low,
For he's my little rabbit,
    Who goes each place I go!

I've hunted in my toy box
    And underneath my chair,
And even in my closet,
    And he's just not anywhere!

It's getting past my bedtime
    And he always sleeps with me.
I just can't sleep without him.
    Wherever can he be?

Oh lookit! There's my bunny!
        He's sound asleep in bed.
I could have guessed he'd be there.
        He's such a sleepyhead!

I'll cuddle up beside him
        While Mommy dims the light.
Oh, my, I'm glad I found him.
        I'm sleepy now . . . goodnight!

Valeria Marcil

Game of One

ONE CUP IS BIGGER THAN ALL THE OTHERS. WHICH ONE IS IT?

ONE HAT IS BIGGER THAN ALL THE OTHERS. WHICH ONE IS IT?

ONE DUCK IS BIGGER THAN ALL THE OTHERS. WHICH ONE IS IT?

1			

WRITE THE NUMBER 1 IN EACH OF THESE BOXES.

Game of Two

TWO SQUIRRELS HAVE BUSHY TAILS. WHICH TWO ARE THEY?

TWO CLOWNS ARE SHORT AND FAT. WHICH TWO ARE THEY?

TWO PUPPIES ARE FAST ASLEEP. WHICH TWO ARE THEY?

WRITE A ROW OF 2'S ON THIS LINE.

2 _____

I Saw a Ship a-Sailing

I saw a ship a-sailing, a-sailing on the sea;
And, oh! it was all laden with pretty things for me!
There were comfits in the cabin, and apples in the hold;
The sails were all of silk, and the masts were made of gold.

The four-and-twenty sailors that stood between the decks,
Were four-and-twenty pretty mice with chains around their necks.
The captain was a duck with a pack upon his back
And when the ship began to move, the captain said, "Quack, quack!"

54

Benjy's Garden

Benjy has a vegetable garden. He takes care of it all by himself. All the vegetables on the table came from Benjy's garden. Can you tell what they are?

Has Benjy got a scarecrow in his garden? Why did he make a scarecrow? Why is Benjy wearing a big straw hat?

What tools do you see? Would you like to have a garden? What vegetables would you like to grow in it?

Which Place is Empty?

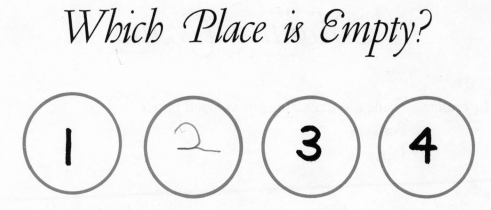

WHICH CIRCLE IS EMPTY? WRITE THE CORRECT NUMBER IN IT.

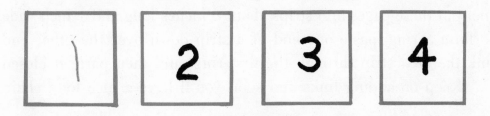

WHICH SQUARE IS EMPTY? WRITE THE CORRECT NUMBER IN IT.

WHICH TRIANGLE IS EMPTY? WRITE THE CORRECT NUMBER IN IT.

WHICH BOX IS EMPTY? WRITE THE CORRECT NUMBER IN IT.

Making Chains

Materials: Some old magazines or colored paper
Scissors
Paste

Colored paper chains are so pretty. They can be used to decorate the house for parties or holidays.

Tear out a few pages of brightly colored pictures from a magazine. Cut these pages into strips about 6 inches long and 1 inch wide. To form a ring, paste one end of a strip down over the other end. Link the next strip through the first ring, and then paste it closed.

Keep on adding links and soon you'll have a nice long chain.

Find the Fawn

Spotty is lost in the middle of a thicket in a dense forest. Can you reach him.

The idea of this game is to put your pencil at the place marked START and to trace a path to Spotty. You must not cross any lines. This means you must keep only in the white spaces. Try it. It's fun!

Johnny the Engineer

BY MARTHA L. NOME

JOHNNY always loved to be a driver.

When he rode his bicycle he'd ring the bell on the handlebars and say:

> "Get out the way!
> Get out the way!
> Here I come!"

People would look up and laugh a little. Then, very slowly they'd step out of his way.

When he rode his scooter he'd shout and say:

"B-r-r-ring! B-r-r-ring!
Get out the way!
Get out the way!
Here I come!"

He had no bell on his scooter. So he had to make the sound of the bell himself. But the people never jumped out of the way fast enough to please Johnny.

When Johnny came down the hill on his skates, he'd shout:

"Get out the way!
Get out the way!
Here I come!"

Johnny liked to go real fast. And if he saw people in the way, he couldn't go as fast as he wanted to.

When Johnny's Daddy took him out in the car, he let Johnny sit on his lap while he drove. He let Johnny help turn the steering wheel. And whenever anyone crossed the street in front of the car, Johnny would blow the horn and shout:

"Get out the way!
Get out the way!
Here we come!"

And everybody would get out of the way and let the car pass.

One afternoon, just before Johnny's birthday, his Daddy came home and said, "I have a birthday present for you. I think you'll like it very much. I'll give it to you tomorrow."

The next morning was Johnny's birthday. He got up early, all happy and excited, for a birthday is a wonderful day.

He ran to his Daddy and said, "*Now* is it time for me to get my present?"

"Yes!" said his Daddy. "Get dressed fast and eat your breakfast. Then we'll go!"

Johnny got dressed fast and ate his breakfast. Then he and his Daddy got into the car and drove off.

"Where are we going?" asked Johnny.

"You'll see," said his Daddy.

Pretty soon, they stopped in front of the railroad station.

"All out!" said his Daddy.

They walked up to the big locomotive where Mr. Johnson, the engineer, was sitting.

"Good morning, Mr. Johnson," said Johnny's Daddy. "Well, here we are!"

"Well, well!" said Mr. Johnson. "Happy birthday, Johnny. How about climbing up here next to me?"

Johnny's Daddy lifted him up, and Mr. Johnson pulled him into the driver's seat right in front.

"Here we go!" said Mr. Johnson.

The train began to hiss and chug.

CHUG! Chug! Chug! Chug!
CHUG! Chug! Chug! Chug!
Hiss! Hiss!

Everybody stepped back from the train. It started to move slowly out of the station. Johnny waved good-bye to his Daddy. Then the train began to move faster.

CHUG!—A-chug—a-chug—chug!
CHUG!—A-chug—a-chug—chug!

it went as it left the station.

"How do you clang the bell?" Johnny asked Mr. Johnson.

"Pull this cord when you want to clang the bell," said Mr. Johnson, "and pull this *other* cord when you want to blow the whistle."

Johnny reached up and pulled the whistle cord.

Toot-toot, ta-too! it went.
Toot-toot, ta-too!
"Get out the way!
Get out the way!

Here we come!" cried Johnny.

The train went still faster. This time it went:

CHOO-choo-choo-choo!
CHOO-choo-choo-choo!

as it sped along the railroad tracks. Nobody *dared* to be in the way.

"Toot-toot, ta-too," went Johnny.
"Clang, clang! Clang, clang!"

Far away he saw a man crossing the tracks. He pulled the whistle cord:

Toot-toot, ta-too!

63

The man looked up and saw the train. He almost jumped off the tracks.

On sped Johnny. In a little while they saw another station.

"Now we slow down," said Mr. Johnson. "Blow the whistle again to let the people in the station know we're coming. Then clang the bell once more, as we pull into the station."

Toot-toot, ta-too!
CLANG! CLANG!
CLANG! CLANG!

Little by little the train began to slow down until it was saying, quite slowly:

Chah! Chah! Chah! Chah!

Then the train stopped. Johnny looked down and there on the station platform was his Daddy waiting for him. His Daddy was smiling happily.

"Oh, Daddy, it was wonderful! Thank you—and Mr. Johnson too—for the most wonderful ride I ever had!"

Pea-Pod Boat

Materials: A pea-pod
2 peas
3 pins
A small piece of cardboard

This little boat is so cute and so easy to make that you can make a whole fleet of them.

Open one long side of a pea-pod. Take out the peas. Now cut a little seat from a piece of cardboard and place it in the boat. It will keep the sides of the boat in position.

To make the little man who rides in the boat, use two peas, one for the head and one for the body. Stick a pin through the peas and then stick the point of the pin into the little cardboard seat. Stick two pins into the bottom pea. These will be the oars with which the little man rows his boat.

If you want these little pea-pod boats to be able to float, paste a piece of adhesive tape or Scotch tape along the bottom to keep out the water.

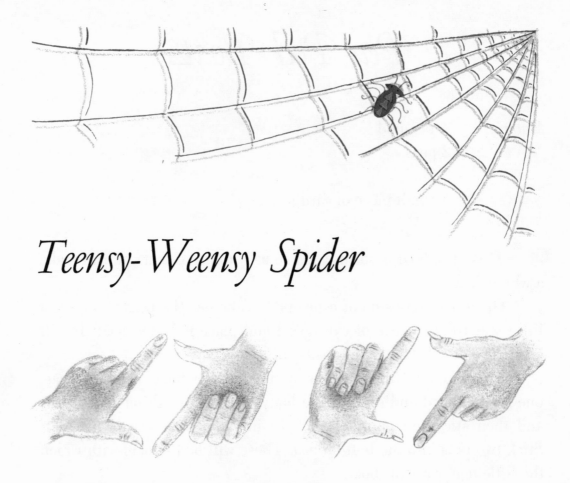

Teensy-Weensy Spider

Place the tip of your right pointer against the tip of your left thumb. Now keeping your fingertips together, twist your hand around and place the tip of your left pointer against the tip of your right thumb, changing back and forth in this way.

A teen-sy ween-sy spi-der ran up the wa-ter

*Now bring both
your hands down.*

*Move both your hands
crossways in front of you.*

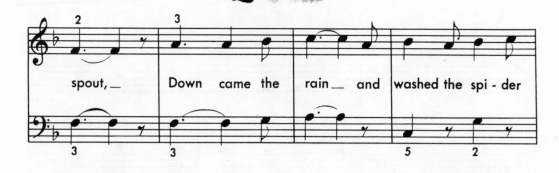

spout, ____ | Down came the | rain __ and | washed the spi - der

*Raise both your hands and
spread your fingers wide, to
look like the rays of the sun.*

out. ___ | Out came the | sun __ and | dried up all the

Bring both hands down. Slap them on your thighs.

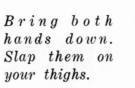

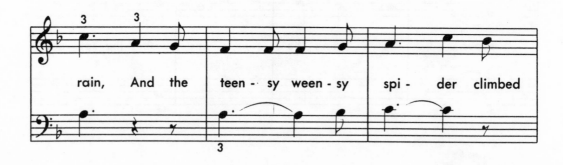

rain,　And the　teen - sy ween - sy　spi - der climbed

Now make your finger climb again as you did at first.

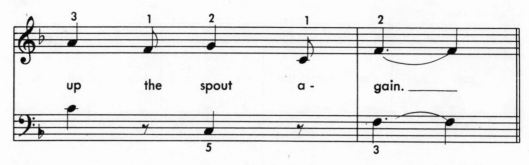

up　the　spout　a -　gain. _____

68

Teddy Bear

Take your pencil and start on dot number one. Draw a line from dot one to dot two. Continue from one dot to another until you have made a complete picture.

Stop and Go

STOP and GO are two words we hear every day. Can you read them when you see them?

This policeman is telling you to STOP. See how he is holding up his hand. The word on his sign says STOP.

This policeman is telling you to GO. See how he is pointing with his hand. The word on his sign says GO.

Here are four different policemen. Look at each one. Who is saying STOP? Who is saying GO?

WRITE THE CORRECT WORD ON EACH POLICEMAN'S SIGN.

Towel Doll

Materials: A towel
Some rags
A piece of string

You can make this cute and cuddlesome rag doll out of a towel. First spread the towel out flat. Then lay a small bunch of clean rags right in the middle of it, as shown in *Picture One*. Gather the towel together under the bunch of rags, to form the round head of your doll. Wind some string or a piece of ribbon under the head and tie it.

Now lift up one corner of the towel and tie it with string or ribbon to form a hand. Do this with the opposite corner of the towel to make the other arm, and your doll will be shaped like the one shown in *Picture Two*. If you like, you can paint or crayon a face on the head of your doll; but face or no face, she will be just as cuddlesome to take to bed with you.

Picture One

Picture Two

The Cow

The cow stands in the big green field,
    She stands there all the day.
I wonder what she thinks about
    While chewing on her hay?

Perhaps about an ice-cream cone?
    Perhaps about a ball?
I wonder what she thinks about,
    Or if she thinks at all!

I guess I'll never know, because
    The cow can't talk, you see.
And if she can, she never, never,
    Never talks to me!

Albert B. Southwick

73

High and Low

WHICH FLOWERS ARE HIGHER? WHICH FLOWERS ARE LOWER?

WHICH AIRPLANE IS HIGHEST? WHICH AIRPLANE IS LOWEST?

WHOSE BED IS HIGHER? WHOSE BED IS LOWER?

WHOSE BLOCKS ARE HIGHER? WHOSE BLOCKS ARE LOWER?

Sliding Basket

Materials: A bucket or basket
Clothesline

Most children have a pail and shovel amongst their toys, or a basket with a handle. You can use either for this play idea.

Slip a piece of clothesline through the handle of a basket or bucket. Then tie one end of the cord to the back of a chair at one side of the room, and tie the other end of the cord to the back of a chair at the other side of the room.

Now when you push the basket, it will slide along the cord from one side of the room to the other. You can put all sorts of things in the basket and then send it sliding across the room to someone who is waiting to receive it.

A sliding basket is very nice to hang next to your bed when you've been sick and must play in bed. You can keep your crayons in it or any other small toys that you want to have near you.

Screwy Tail

Down in a pen in the Ingle field
　　Lived as fat a piggy as ever squealed!
Almost as round as a ball was he,
　　And pink all over as he could be.

And because of the way his tail would twirl,
　　And twist around like a little curl,
Johnny Ingle and his sister Gail
　　Gave him the name of Screwy Tail.

Now the only language this pig could speak
　　Was just two words, UNK and EEK,
And if all the meanings of EEK and UNK
　　Could be written down, they'd fill a trunk!

"UNK! (Good morning, it's a pretty day!)
        UNK! (This is right good food, I'll say!)
(Watch me fall in this mud, kerplunk!
        Why don't you try it?) UNK, UNK, UNK!"

Those were only a few of the things
        Screwy Tail meant by his UNK-UNKings.
But oh, how very diff-er-ent
        Were the various things that EEK, EEK meant!

"EEK! (you get away from here!)
        EEK! (I'm scared to death, oh dear!")
And you always knew when he EEKed real bad
        That something had scared or made him mad.

Now Johnny Ingle and his sister Gail
    Were ever so proud of Screwy Tail;
For they had bought him from Mister Sloan
    With five dollar bills of their very own.

They'd raised and fed him to make him big,
    So he'd become a blue ribbon pig.
And they took him off to the country fair,
    To show him to the judges there.

But oh, that pig! He EEKed and EEKed!
    "I just don't want to go!" he shrieked.
"I want to stay in my own square pen!
    Why don't you take me back again?"

But when Screwy Tail saw at the country fair
　　That his EEKs weren't getting him anywhere,
He UNKed and UNKed for the rest of the day
　　And behaved in the friendliest kind of way.

　　And he won a prize, did Screwy Tail,
　　　　To the great delight of Johnny and Gail.
　　Said Johnny, "He won it because he's fat,
　　　　And well-proportioned, on top of that."

Quoth Gail, "Because he's pretty, too!
　　Screwy Tail, we're so proud of you!"
"UNK," grunted Screwy, "that's the bunk!
　　I won because I started to UNK!"

Helen Pettigrew

Sing a Song of Sixpence

The king was in the counting house
Counting out his money,
The queen was in the parlor
Eating bread and honey,
The maid was in the garden
Hanging out the clothes,
Along came a blackbird
And snipped off her nose.

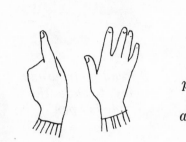

Hold up six fingers.

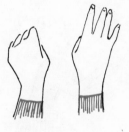

Tap your pocket with your hand a few times.

Not too fast

Sing a song of six - pence A pock - et full of rye,

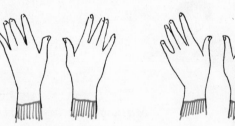

Hold up four fingers.

Then hold up ten fingers twice, to make twenty-four

Four and twen - ty black - birds Baked in a pie.

81

Pretend you are
cutting a slice
of pie.

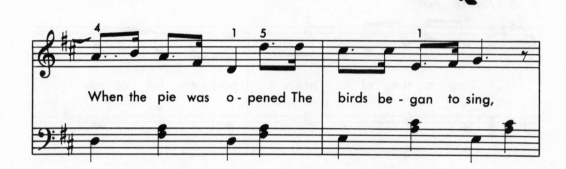

Spread your hands
wide, to show the
pie is open.

When the pie was o - pened The birds be - gan to sing,

Make a bow or a curtsy, holding
out your arms in front of you, as
though you are offering a pie to
the King.

Was - n't that a dain - ty dish to set be - fore the King?

Doily Delight

Materials: Paper doilies
Crayons or paints

Ask Mother for some of those paper doilies that she puts under a cake. A whole package of them costs only ten cents, so Mother will certainly be glad to let you have a few.

It's easy to decorate these doilies prettily, because all you have to do is follow the design on the doily. If the doily is in a floral pattern you might color the leaves green and the flowers different colors; or you may wish to color the center part of the doily in one color, and the border in another color.

Mother would be so pleased with a matching set to use as place mats under the dishes at breakfast or lunch.

Zoo Fun

Here's another dot game. If you know how to count, you can solve it.

Put your pencil on the dot marked 1, then draw a line from dot 1 to dot 2. Continue in this way, drawing your next line from dot 2 to dot 3, on to dot 4 and so forth. When you get to dot 48, connect it with dot 1.

After you've connected all the dots, you'll have a nice surprise picture.

this is a

Different Ages

In each group, there is one thing which is youngest, one which is oldest, and one which is in between. Can you tell which is the youngest in each group? Can you tell which is the oldest?

The Squirrel's Thank-You Present

BY MARTHA L. NOME

ANNETTE and her brother, Jackie, had just come to the country for the summer. They loved the country.

There was a little stream behind their house. One of the things they liked best was wading in this stream.

One day, Annette was sitting on a stone, cooling her feet in the stream. Suddenly she heard a little crying sound. She looked all around, and she finally found where the crying came from. It came from a tiny baby squirrel who was lying between two large stones. She quickly put on her shoes and socks and ran over to see what the trouble was.

It was trouble, all right, for the little squirrel's leg was hurt. He couldn't even walk. Very gently, she picked him up and carried him home.

"Oh, poor thing," said Jackie, when he saw the squirrel. "His leg is hurt. Do you think it will get better?"

"Well, we must let him rest for a few weeks," Annette answered. "We'll keep him in the house and bring his food to him. Then he won't have to run on his leg, looking for things to eat."

"Okay," said Jackie. "I'll get a box to keep him in."

Jackie found a large cardboard box and filled it with straw. Annette put the squirrel in it, and gave him some nuts and acorns to eat. The tiny squirrel was happy and comfortable.

Annette cared for him each day. After two weeks he got so used to her, that he would eat right out of her hand.

One day, she came home and found his box was empty. She called and called and looked all over, but she could not find him. You can imagine how badly she felt. In a very sad mood, she walked down to the stream where she had found him and sat down to think. All of a sudden, she heard a happy chirping sound. She looked up and there was her little squirrel. He was sitting up so cutely on his hind legs.

"Where have you been? Why did you run away?" she asked him.

The little squirrel cocked his head to one side and looked at her. He jumped down off his stone and ran along the grass a little distance. Then he stopped, got up on his hind legs again and chirruped — for all the world as if he were trying to speak to Annette.

Annette followed him. As soon as she got close to him, he ran off a little further. Then he stopped and chirruped at her, just as if to say, "Follow me."

In this way, Annette followed the little squirrel. Suddenly he stopped at the foot of a ladder. The ladder was nailed to a great big tree. As soon as he saw that Annette was catching up to him, he scurried up the ladder. Annette climbed right up after him!

As she stepped up to the top step, she found herself in the coziest little tree house you ever saw! There was a little table and two little chairs in it. And a window!

She went over to the window and looked out. Oh, it was like being on the top of the world! She could look down over the whole countryside. She could see the stream and the farmers' houses and the cows in the fields. And she could see the house she lived in. There was her Mommy, out in the garden!

She turned to the little squirrel to tell him how wonderful it was — but he was gone. Then she understood. This was the little squirrel's thank-you present for taking care of him when he was hurt.

All summer long Annette and her brother Jackie played in the tree house. They had many happy times there. At last, the end of the summer came. It was time for Annette and Jackie to go back to the city.

"Let's give the squirrel a good-bye present," said Jackie. And Annette agreed. So they gathered a basketful of nuts and put it in the tree house, hoping the squirrel would find it. If he did, he would have plenty to eat during the long winter.

And sure enough, the squirrel came and found the nuts.

First, Second, Third

Color the first house red. Color the second house blue.
Color the third house green.

Color the first flower yellow. Color the second flower purple.
Color the third flower red. Color the last one blue.

Color the first clock blue. Color the second clock green.
Color the third clock orange. Color the rest brown.

Color the first fish orange. Color the second fish green.
Color the third fish red. Color the rest blue.

The Mouse Who Didn't Like Cheese

I heard a tale of a cute little mouse
    Who was ever so hard to please;
He was fond of spinach, and peas, and corn,
    But he just didn't care for cheese!

The mice of the world, both near and far,
    Whispered, "Now, what's all this?
Can it really be true there's a mousie who
    Runs away from a piece of Swiss?"

And the mice of the world, both far and near,
    Were caught in the traps of men;
They left their homes for a bit of cheese,
    And they never came back again.

Except for that very particular mouse,
    The cutie who wouldn't eat cheese —
He's running about, as free as a bird,
    And lives in contentment and ease.

They laughed at this silly, silly mouse,
    For dining on spinach and peas;
But today, he happily scampers about,
    Just because he doesn't like cheese!

Stephen Schlitzer

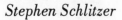

What Are They Used For?

WHAT IS USED FOR TELLING TIME?

WHAT IS USED FOR MAKING MUSIC?

WHAT IS USED FOR SLEEPING?

WHAT IS USED FOR LETTING IN LIGHT?

WHAT IS USED FOR CUTTING THE GRASS?

WHAT IS USED FOR COOKING?

WHAT IS USED FOR EATING?

WHAT IS USED FOR CARRYING THINGS?

Clothespins-on-the-Line

Materials: A length of clothesline
                About 10 clothespins
                2 chairs

Clothespin fun can be enjoyed both indoors and outdoors. On a rainy day you will feel less boxed in if you play this game.

Tie a piece of clothesline to the backs of two sturdy chairs. Ask Mother for about ten clothespins. You can clip them on the line and slide them back and forth.

Then you can hang your doll's clothes on the line and some socks or handkerchiefs that Mother will give you.

Who Uses What?

Here are pictures of four different kinds of people. Do you know what they do? Point to the things that the woodsman uses in his work. Point to the things that the soldier should be holding. What does the cowboy use in his work? What does the fisherman use to catch fish?

Pillow Snow-Man

Materials: A pillow
            Cord or ribbon
            Odd bits of colored cloth
            Safety pins

It's so easy to make this home-made snow-man to play with. Take a nice big bed-pillow with its white pillowcase on it. Tie off the top third of the pillow with cord or ribbon. This will form the snow-man's head. Now pin or sew two little patches of colored cloth on the snow-man's face for eyes. Use another strip of cloth for the nose, and another for the mouth.

Place a jaunty hat on the snow-man's head. Sit him on a chair and you're all set for winter fun even if it's midsummer.

Tommy Mouse Maze

Tommy Mouse has found his way into the storehouse where the grain is kept. Can you reach him before he opens the grain bag?

The idea of the game is to put your pencil at the place marked START and to trace a path to the granary, where Tommy Mouse is getting ready to feed himself. You must not cross any lines. This means you must keep only in the white spaces. See if you can beat Tommy Mouse to the grain bag!

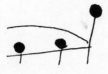

Lazy

I wish I were electrified —
    I wouldn't have to worry;
For everything I had to do
    I'd then do in a hurry.

I'd have a dozen buttons spread
    In rows across my chest;
I'd press one in the morning
    And presto! I'd be dressed!

I'd want one that would wash my teeth;
    And one to comb my hair;
And one to get me off to school,
    And help with lessons there!

Ruth H. Galgano

Floating Soap Boat

Materials: A bar of floating soap
　　　　　　5 lollypop sticks
　　　　　　Some wooden matches
　　　　　　Some corks
　　　　　　Knife or a single-edged razor blade
　　　　　　Crayons

Soak a piece of floating soap in warm water to make it soft enough so that you can force lollypop sticks into it. Push one stick into the narrow end of the cake. Then push three sticks into the top side of the soap. The middle stick should be a little higher than the

other two. Push a fifth stick into the other narrow end of the soap, but tilt this stick up at an angle. None of these sticks should be more than 3 inches long or else your boat will be top-heavy and turn over.

Now tie a piece of string from the first stick to the second stick —and so on, until you have connected all five sticks.

To make the cute little cork sailors, break off the heads of some wooden matches. Whittle the ends of the matches to a point. Stick two of them into the sides of the cork to form the arms and then stick two longer pieces into the bottom of the cork to form the legs. Make both ends of the legs sharp. Then you can stick them into the soap deck and your sailors won't fall overboard. Of course, it doesn't matter much if they do for they can't drown—they just float around! Use crayons to draw happy little mouths, eyes and noses on the little cork men.

Little Horace

Here's another dot game. If you know how to count, you can solve it.

Put your pencil on the dot marked 1, then draw a line from dot 1 to dot 2. Continue in this way, drawing your next line from dot 2 to dot 3, on to dot 4 and so forth.

After you've connected all the dots, you'll have a nice surprise picture.

Right to the Finish

Dotty and Dan saw the peas and the pan
 And said to their mother, "We'll shell 'em!"
Then the pea pods went pop! and the green peas went hop!
 Said Dotty, "It's fun to expel 'em!"

But their fingers grew tired, their interest expired —
 They were longing to run out and play.
"Oh, gee, Dan, I wish we could go catch some fish,"
 Cried Dotty, "Let's up and away!"

But I'm glad to relate they decided to wait
 Till they shelled all the peas in the pan;
If there's something you start, you must do your part,
 And finish the job you began!

Helen Waite Munro

Toothpick Pictures

Materials: Toothpicks

You can make all kinds of pictures and designs out of toothpicks. Just lay them on the floor or table in the shapes you like. You can break the toothpicks in half when you want to make shorter lines. On this page you will see a few ideas for pictures; but you will think of many more ideas yourself.

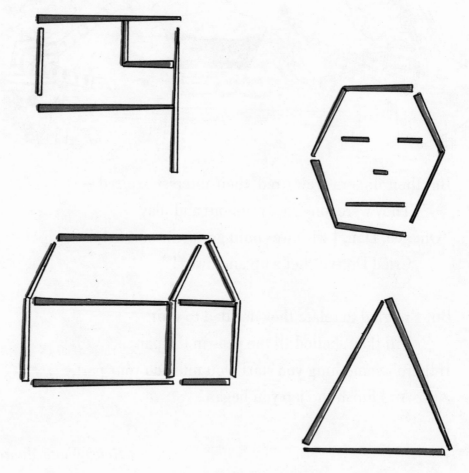

A Present for Mother

On this page, you see six different things. Which things are made of wood? Which are not made of wood? What do you think Billy's mother would like to have for her birthday?

Things That Go Together

Each of the six things above the line go with one of the things below the line. For example, the comb goes with the brush. Can you tell what belongs with what?

One's and Two's

HOW MANY HORSES ARE BLACK?　Write the number in this box.

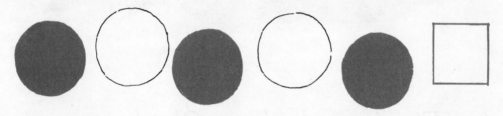

HOW MANY BABIES ARE CRYING?　Write the number in this box.

HOW MANY BALLS ARE WHITE?　Write the number in this box.

1

Write a row of 1's on this line.

2

Write a row of 2's on this line.

Timi and the Elephant

BY CLEMENTINA LONG

ONCE there was a little boy named *Timi* who lived in India. *Timi* lived in a little straw hut in the jungle, all by himself.

One day, when he was sitting in front of his hut, he heard a big noise. He looked up, and there, coming out of the jungle was a big elephant. The elephant's name was *Bingo*. The elephant had something on his back, something big and wooden. *Timi* didn't know what it was, so he asked him.

"Hello," said *Timi*, "What's that on your back?"

"That's a house," said the elephant. "Do you want to see it?"
"Oh, yes!" said *Timi*. So the elephant stretched out his long

trunk, and wrapped it around *Timi's* waist, and lifted him up high
in the air, all the way up to the little house on his back.

Timi peeked through the curtains into the house and saw a
little bed with a big pillow and a pretty quilt. Right over the bed

was a shelf of toys and books. Then there was a little table and a chair, and on top of the table, there was a tiny cupboard for food. And best of all, hanging from the ceiling was a bell-rope. You just had to pull the rope and a big bell would go *Clang-Clang!* That was

so everybody would get out of the way when *Bingo,* the elephant, came through. There also was a little folding ladder that could stretch

all the way down to the ground. It would be lots of fun to climb up and down this wonderful little ladder.

Timi thought it was the nicest house he'd ever seen. "Oh," he said, "How I'd love to live here!"

"That's just what I hoped you'd say," said *Bingo*, "I'm so lonesome all by myself, I'd love to have you live with me."

"Me, too," said *Timi*. So *Timi* went to live in the house on top of the elephant. And they both went off into the jungle as happy as could be. *Timi* sat up in front and rang the bell just for fun. "Everybody get out of the way," he cried. "We're coming through!"

It was a very hot day. Soon they came to a river. *Bingo* asked *Timi*, "How would you like a nice, cool shower?" *Timi* said he'd love it. So the elephant stretched up his trunk, wrapped it around *Timi's* waist and carried him *Wheeeee!* through the air down to the ground. Then *Bingo* sucked up a lot of water from the river into his long trunk, and gave *Timi* a wonderful cold shower. My, that was fun!

Afterwards, *Timi* sat up on top of *Bingo's* head to get dry. Then *Bingo* took him across the river. *Bingo* was so big, they didn't need a boat or a bridge or anything — *Bingo* just *walked* across.

Timi was very happy living in the jungle, in the little house on *Bingo's* back. *Bingo* was almost as high as the tree tops, and so *Timi* was able to talk to the birds just by looking out of his window. Sometimes the birds used to fly in and eat breakfast with him. He never had to worry about food, either. He could just reach out and pick bananas and coconuts off the trees. He made friends with the monkeys and they used to show him where the best coconuts were.

One day, they came to a big city. When they walked through the streets all the people stared at them. They had never seen any-one who lived in a house on top of an elephant. All the little boys in the city wished that they could live the way *Timi* did. They begged him to let them come up and see his house. So he unrolled the little ladder and invited them to come up, one at a time to visit his house.

A few days later, a man from the circus heard about *Timi's* house and came to visit him.

"My," said the man, "what a wonderful house — and such a fine elephant. Won't you both come and be part of my circus?"

"Well, I don't know." said *Timi*. "We are very happy here."

"But," the man answered, "we have all kinds of wonderful things in our circus."

"You have!" said *Timi*. "What kind of wonderful things?"

"Well," said the man,

"We have the fattest lady in the world!

And the skinniest man in the world!

We have dozens of gay clowns and pretty dancers, who are great fun to watch.

We have the smallest man in the world — he wouldn't come up to your shoulder!

And we have wonderful tightrope walkers who dance on a rope — way up in the air!

And marvelous bare-back riders! The circus horses ride around so fast! And the riders stand right on the horses' backs. The horses

dance to the music, and prance around with two feet held high in the air.

We have three funny seals that balance golden balls on their noses! They can even make the balls twirl around.

And we have a clever poodle who does all kinds of tricks. He can sit up and beg. He can stand on his two hind legs and dance — he can even jump through a hoop as quickly as a rabbit!

We have a great, big lion who can roar much louder than your elephant. We have all kinds of wonderful things in this circus, but we *never* had a little boy living in a house on top of an elephant's back. Please come and be in our circus."

"Will you take care of me and *Bingo,* and make sure that he gets enough to eat?" *Timi* asked.

119

"I promise that I will," answered the man.

"All right, then," said *Timi*. "I'll come and be part of your circus."

And that's just what *Timi* did! Next time you go to the circus, look for an elephant with a house on his back, and that's where you'll find *Timi*.

Secret Hiding Place

Materials: 4 chairs
A blanket or a sheet

Take four chairs and arrange them in two rows, back to back, with a little space between them. Throw a blanket or a sheet over the chairs. Place some books or heavy objects on the blanket where it falls over the seats of the chairs, so that the blanket won't slip out of place.

The blanket will form the roof of a little tent. It's fun to crawl in and out of this secret hiding place. You can bring your toys in there and play all sorts of make-believe games.

Ten Tiny Men

I have ten little tiny men
        Who work all day for me.
They dress me up from head to toe
        As nicely as can be.

They wash my face, and comb my hair
        And keep me nice and neat.
They cut my food and serve me well
        When I sit down to eat.

From morn to night, in every way
        They're busy little men
You have them too, if you just knew —
        Why, they're your fingers ten!

Florence Wedge

The Nest

Here's another dot game. If you know how to count, you can solve it.

Put your pencil on the dot marked 1, then draw a line from dot 1 to dot 2. Continue in this way, drawing your next line from dot 2 to dot 3, on to dot 4 and so forth.

After you've connected all the dots, you'll have a nice surprise picture.

Winter and Summer

Look at all the pictures on this page. Point to all the things we see in the summertime. Point to all the things we see in the wintertime.

Chicky-Dee!

Here's another dot game. If you know how to count, you can solve it.

Put your pencil on the dot marked 1, then draw a line from dot 1 to dot 2. Continue in this way, drawing your next line from dot 2 to dot 3, on to dot 4 and so forth.

After you've connected all the dots, you'll have a nice surprise picture.

The Gingerbread Man

I'm going to bake a gingerbread man—
With Mother's help, I'm sure I can.
Flour and sugar and spices all go
Into the bowl to make my dough.
A little of this and some of that,
Mix and stir and roll the dough flat.

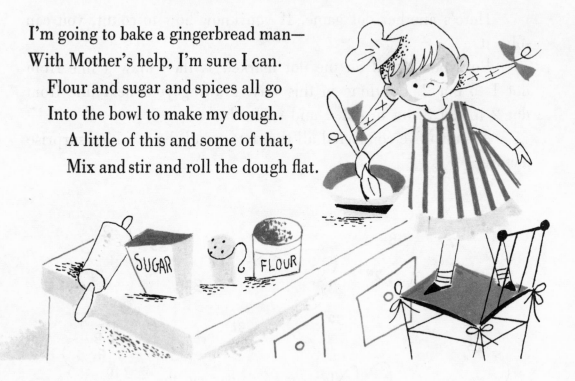

Shape the man with a cookie cutter
And grease the pan with lots of butter.
Raisin eyes and a cherry nose!
He's finished and into the oven he goes.
The heat will turn him a golden brown
And soon as he's done, I'll gobble him down!

Shirley Mann

Walnut Fleet

Materials: 2 halves of a walnut shell
2 toothpicks
Paper
Gum or melted crayon
Scissors
Paper matches

To make a fleet, clean out the half shells of some walnuts. Anchor the toothpick mast with a small piece of chewed gum or some melted crayon. Cut out a small piece of paper to make the sails. If you color the sails on both sides with crayon, they will be both water-proof and pretty. Stick the sail on the toothpick mast—and your ship is done!

A cute little passenger can be made by drawing features on a paper match, as shown in *Picture One*. Then cut the match, as shown in *Picture Two*. Crease his legs to make his knees bend and fold the match at the hips, so that he can sit in his boat, as shown in *Picture Three*.

Picture One   *Picture Two*   *Picture Three*

HART

PUBLISHING

COMPANY

Barbara
Sue